Tales of Cornish
Witchcraft

Robert Hunt

Bossiney Books • Exeter

Robert Hunt

Robert Hunt (1807-1887) was a scientist and poet, born in Devonport. His father was a naval officer who drowned while Robert was still a child. He studied as a chemist in London, but became ill in 1828, and moved back to convalesce in Cornwall, where he gathered folk-lore tales.

In 1840 he was appointed secretary to the Royal Cornwall Polytechnic Society in Falmouth, then became keeper of mining records at the Museum of Economic Geology in London, where he also lectured.

At the same time he was an early pioneer of photography, publishing a *Manual of Photography* in 1841, and wrote poetry.

In 1865 he published *Popular Romances of the West of England or the drolls, traditions and superstitions of old Cornwall*, drawing on his own research and that of Thomas Quiller Couch and William Bottrell. The present book is entirely drawn from this source. Minor editorial changes have been made, in particular to place-name spellings.

Other Bossiney books by Robert Hunt

Tales of Cornish Giants
Tales of Cornish Mariners and Mermaids

This reprint 2023
First published 2021 byBossiney Books Ltd,
68 Thorndale Courts, Whitycombe Way, Exeter, Devon, EX4 2NY
www.bossineybooks.com
© 2021 Bossiney Books Ltd   All rights reserved
ISBN 978-1-915664-23-5
Printed in Great Britain by Deltor, Saltash, Cornwall

Belief in witchcraft in the Victorian period

That a deep-rooted belief in the power of the witch still lingers in the remote districts of Cornwall cannot be denied. A gentleman, who has for many years been actively engaged in a public capacity, gives me, in reply to some questions which I put to him relative to a witch or conjurer, much information, which is embodied in this section.

A 'cunning man' was long resident in Bodmin, to whom the people from all parts of the country went to be relieved of spells, under the influence of which either themselves or their cattle were supposed to be suffering.

Thomas —— , who resided at Nanstallan, not far from the town of Bodmin, was waylaid, robbed, and well thrashed on his way home from market. This act, which was accompanied by some appearance of brutality, was generally attributed to one of the dupes of his cunning. Howbeit, Thomas —— appears to have felt that the place was getting too hot for him, for he migrated to one of the parishes on the western side of the Fowey river.

Numerous instances are within my knowledge of the belief which existed amongst the peasantry that this man really possessed the power of removing the effects of witchcraft. Thomas —— took up his abode for some time with a small farmer, who had lost some cattle. These losses were attributed to the malign influences of some evil-disposed person; but as Thomas —— failed to detect the individual, he with the farmer made many journeys to Exeter, to consult the 'White Witch' who resided in that city. Whether the result was satisfactory or otherwise, I have never learned.

Thomas —— , it must be remembered, was only a 'witch.' The term is applied equally to men as to women. I never heard any uneducated person speak of a 'wizard'. There appear to be, however, some very remarkable distinctions between a male and a female witch. The former is almost always employed to remove the evil influences exerted by the latter. Witches such as Thomas had but limited power. They could tell who had been guilty of ill-wishing, but they were powerless to break the spell and 'unbewitch' the sufferer. This was frequently accomplished by the friends of the bewitched, who, in concert with Thomas —— , would perform certain ceremonies, many of them of an obscene, and usually of blasphemous, character.

The 'White Witch' was supposed to possess the higher power of removing the spell, and of punishing the individual by whose wickedness the wrong had been inflicted.

Jenny Harris was a reputed witch. This woman, old, poor and, from the world's ill usage, rendered malicious, was often charged with the evils which fell upon cattle, children, or, indeed, on men and women. On one occasion, a robust and rough-handed washerwoman, who conceived that she was under the spell of Jenny Harris, laid violent hands on the aged crone, being resolved to 'bring blood from her'. The witch's arm was scratched and gouged from the elbow to the wrist, so that a sound inch of skin did not exist. This violent assault became the subject of inquiry before the magistrates, who fined the washerwoman five pounds for the assault.

My correspondent writes: I was also present at a magistrates' meeting at the Porcupine Inn, near Tywardreath, some years ago, when an old woman from Golant was brought up for witchcraft. One farmer, who appeared against her, stated that he had then six bullocks hanging up in chains in his orchard, and he attributed their disease and death to the poor old woman's influence. The case was dismissed, but it afforded a good deal of merriment. There was a dinner at the inn after the meeting, and some of the farmers present were disposed to ridicule the idea of witchcraft.

I said, well knowing their real views and opinions, 'Gentlemen, it is all well enough to laugh, but it appears to me to be a serious matter.'

Upon which Mr —— , a farmer of —— , said, 'You are right, Mr —— ; I'll tell of two cases in which one family suffered severely,' and he gave us the details of the cases. All the others present had a case or two, each one within his own experience to vouch for, and the whole afternoon was spent telling witch stories.

The extent to which this belief was carried within a comparatively recent period, may be inferred from the fact that, on one occasion when the visitors were assembled at the county asylum, a man residing at Callington came with the mother of a poor imbecile patient, and sent his card to the boardroom. This was inscribed with his name and M.A. Upon being asked how he became a Master of Arts, he replied that he was a 'Master of Black Arts'. The object of this fellow's visit was, having persuaded the mother of his power, to propose to the visitors that they should place the imbecile girl in his care, upon his undertaking, on their paying him five pounds, to cure her. Of course this was not listened to. This fellow imposed upon people to such an extent that he was eventually tried at the sessions, under an almost forgotten Act of Parliament, for witchcraft. The impression on the mind of my informant is that the case broke down.

In confirmation of the melancholy facts related of the continuance of the belief in witchcraft, I would give the accompanying cuttings from the *West Briton* newspaper of a very recent date:

Gross Superstition

During the week ending Sunday last, a 'wise man' from Illogan has been engaged with about half-a-dozen witchcraft cases, one a young tradesman, and another a sea-captain. It appears that the 'wise man' was in the first place visited at his home by these deluded people at different times, and he declared the whole of them to be spell-bound. In one case he said that if the person had not come so soon, in about a fortnight he would have been in the asylum; another would have had his leg broken; in every case something very direful would have happened.

Numerous incantations have been performed. In the case of a captain of a vessel, a visit was paid to the sea-side, and while the 'wise man' uttered some unintelligible gibberish, the captain had to throw a stone into the sea. So heavy was the spell under which he laboured, and which immediately fell upon the 'wise man', that the latter pretended that he could scarcely walk back to Hayle.

The most abominable part of the incantations is performed during the hours of midnight, and for that purpose the wretch sleeps with his victims, and for five nights following he had five different bed-fellows. Having no doubt reaped a pretty good harvest during the week, he returned to his home on Monday; but such was the pretended effect produced by the different spells and witchcraft that fell upon him from his many dupes, that two of the young men who had been under his charge were obliged to obtain a horse and cart and carry him to the Hayle station. One of the men, having had 'two spells' resting on him, the 'wise man' was obliged to sleep with him on Saturday and Sunday nights, having spent the whole of the Sunday in his diabolical work. It is time that the police, or some other higher authorities, should take the matter up, as the person alluded to is well known, and frequently visited by the ignorant and superstitious.

The case of Gross Superstition at Hayle

In the *West Briton* of the 27th ult. we gave some particular of several cases of disgraceful fraud and delusion which had been practised by a pretended 'wise man' from Illogan, and of gross superstition and gullibility on the part of his dupes. A correspondent has furnished us with the following particulars relative to the antecedents of the pretended conjurer. He states that James Thomas, the conjurer from the parish of Illogan, married some time since the late celebrated Tammy Blee [1793-1856], of Redruth, who afterwards removed to Helston and carried on as a fortune-teller, but parted from her husband, James Thomas, on account of a warrant for his apprehension having been issued against him by the magistrates of St Ives, for attempting to take a spell from Mrs Paynter, through her husband, William Paynter, who stated before the magistrates that he wanted to commit a disgraceful offence.

Thomas then absconded, and was absent from the west of Cornwall for upwards of two years. His wife then stated that the virtue was in her and not in him; that she was of the real 'pellar' blood; and that he could tell nothing but through her. His greatest dupes have been at St Just and Hayle, and other parts of the west of Cornwall. He has been in the habit of receiving money annually for keeping witchcraft from vessels sailing out of Hayle. He slept with several of his dupes recently; and about a fortnight since he stated that he must sleep with certain young men at Copperhouse, Hayle, in order to protect them from something that was hanging over them, one of them being a mason and another a miner, the two latter lately from St Just. He said himself this week at Truro that he had cured a young man of St Erth, and was going on Saturday again to take a spell from the father, a tin smelter.

He has caused a great disturbance amongst the neighbours, by charging some with having bewitched others. He is a drunken, disgraceful, beastly fellow, and ought to be sent to the treadmill. One of the young men is now thoroughly ashamed of himself to think he has been duped so by this scoundrel. We have purposely withheld the names of a number of Thomas's egregious dupes, with which our correspondent has furnished us, believing that the badgering which they have doubtless received from their friends has proved a sufficient punishment to them, and that their eyes are now thoroughly opened to the gross and disgraceful imposture that has been practised upon them.'

The following is from the *Western Morning News*

At the Liskeard police court, on Monday, Harriet King appeared before the sitting magistrates charged with an assault on Elizabeth Wellington. The complainant had called the mother of defendant a witch, and said she had ill-wished a person, and the ill wish fell on the cat, and the cat died. This annoyed the daughter, who retaliated by bad words and blows. The magistrates expressed surprise at the cause of the assault, but as that had been proved, they fined defendant 1s. and the costs, £1 in all.

Ill wishing

I give the following notices as I receive them:

'I caant altogether exackly bleve in wiches at al,' said a good dame to us; 'but this I can tell ee, our John's wife quarrelled once with her next door neighbour's wife, and when John come home, like a husband always should, he took up for his wife, northin but nat'r'l chiel was a. Well, the woman took a nif, and for a long time never spoke to our John; at laast, after a bit, she used to speak to un, and like as if a was all over, and she used to speak quite sochebl-like.

'Well, John alleas was very well when he used to meet her, but as soon as ever he got underground, he was tooken ill to wonce; when a dedn't meet her, a was well enuf. Well, John was advised to go to the Pellar, and off he went to Helstun sure nuf, and the Pellar towld un to come so many times in three months, and do something anorther, and towld un who a was that hoverlooked un, and a was that vere woman. Well, the Pellar towld John that if a dedn't do it, a would very likely die sudden. Our John, dear fellow, came home, and got unbelieving, and dedn't do as a was towld. Wat was the konsikense? Why, in less than three months a was a dead man.

'Not as I believe the woman's a witch—no, not I; but she had a evil mind, and what's so bad as a evil mind?'

'I used to have a woman meeting me,' said a fisherman, 'when I went a-fishing; and she used to wish me "a good catch" every time she seed me, and I was always sure to have no luck whenever I met her; luck used to be good enough other times. Well, I went to the Pellar, and done what he told me I done, and the woman came and begged my pardon, and my luck was good enough after that.'

To what purpose he had been lucky I could not divine, for he was miserably clad, and I learned that his family were, like himself, miserable and degraded.

In a certain cordwainer's workshop, which we could name, the following important information was afforded by a lady customer. The worthy tradesman was bewailing the loss of a good-sized pig that had sickened, and being afraid it would die, he had drowned it, to make its death easier: 'If thee'st only towld me afore, tha peg wud a bean wel enuf in a week, I knaw. That peg wus begruged thee, thas the way a wudn' thrive. I'll tel ee wat mi faathur dun wonse. He wont hof to pausans [parson's] an' bot a bra purty letle peg, an' as a wus cumin home wed'en, a womun seed un, an' axed faathur to sell un to hur fur five shelins fur his bargin. Shaan't sell un, saze faathur. Mite sa wel, saze she, an' off she went. Faathur tendud un an' tended un, an' a wudn' grough a mossel. Wy? A was begruged, thas wot a was. Wel, faathur wen' off, an' he wos towld to go hom an fill a botel with waater, an' bere un in the cawl. Faathur dun so, an' a wuden long afore the wumun caame to faathur an' axed un wat had a dun by hur, for she suffered agonies; an' if heed only 'forgive' hur, she'd nevur do so nevur no mure. So faathur went to the cawl hus, an' brok the botel. She was at once relieved, an' the peg got wel enuf aftur. I can tel ee, ef thee's honle dun that, a wud ben wel enuf, if a wusn'd pisind.'

'Well,' said one of the company, 'I believe I was ill-wished once. I had a great beautiful cage, full of pretty canaries. I hung them out one Sunday morning, and a woman came along and asked me to let her have one of my birds. "Yes," said I, "for half-a-crown." She said she shouldn't buy none. I told her I would not give her one, and off she went. That day week I had not a bird left; everybody said they was bethought me, and I suppose they were; but this I do know, I lost all my canaries.'

The 'Pellar'

A man who has resided at several places on the south coast was known by this name. He is said to be in possession of no end of charms, and to possess powers, of no common order, over this and the other world.

'He is able,' writes a friend, 'to put ghosts, hobgoblins, and, I believe, even Satan himself, to rest. I have known farmers, well informed in many other matters, and members of religious bodies, go to the Pellar to have the "spirits that possessed the calves" driven out; for they, the calves, were so wild, they tore down all the wooden fences and gates, and must be possessed with the devil.

'The Pellar always performs a cure; but as the evil spirits must go somewhere, and as it is always to be feared that they may enter into other calves or pigs, or, it may be, even possess the bodies of their owners themselves, the Pellar makes it imperative that a stone wall shall be built around the calves, to confine them for three times seven days, or until the next moon is as old as the present one. This precaution always results in taming the devils and the calves, and consequently in curing them – the Pellar usually sending the spirits to some very remote region, and chaining them down under granite rocks.'

'An old woman had long suffered from debility; but she and her friends were satisfied that she had been ill-wished. So she went to the Pellar. He told her to buy a bullock's heart, and get a packet of pound pins. She was to stick the heart as full of pins as she could, and "the body that ill-wished her felt every pin run into the bullock's heart same as if they had been run into her." The spell was taken off, and the old woman grew strong.'

'An old man living on Lady Downs had a lot of money stolen from his house. He, too, went to the Pellar. In this case the magician performed the spells, and the man was told the money would be returned. After a few days, it was so; the money, during the night, was tied to the handle of the door, and found there by the owner in the morning.'

Bewitched cattle

A farmer, who possessed broad acres, and who was in many respects a sensible man, was greatly annoyed to find that his cattle became diseased in the spring. Nothing could satisfy him but that they were bewitched, and he was resolved to find out the person who had cast the evil eye on his oxen. According to an anciently prescribed rule, the farmer took one of his bullocks and bled it to death, catching all the blood on bundles of straw. The bloody straw was then piled into a heap, and set on fire. Burning with a vast quantity of smoke, the farmer expected to see the witch, either in reality or in shadow, amidst the smoke.

In this particular case he was to some extent gratified. An old woman who lived in the adjoining village noticing the fire and smoke and – with all a woman's curiosity – went to Farmer ——'s field to see what was going on.

She was instantly pounced on by this superstitious man, and he would no doubt have seriously ill-treated her, had not the poor, and now terrified, old soul, who roused her neighbours by her cries, been rescued by them. Every person knew this poor woman to be a most inoffensive and good creature, and consequently the farmer was only laughed at for sacrificing thus foolishly one of his oxen.

How to become a witch

Touch a Logan stone nine times at midnight, and any woman will become a witch. A more certain plan is said to be to get on the Giant's Rock at Zennor Church-Town nine times without shaking it. Seeing that this rock was at one time a very sensitive Logan stone, the task was somewhat difficult.

Cornish sorcerers

The powers of the sorcerer appear to have been passed on from father to son through a long succession of generations. There are many families – the descendants from the ancient Cornish people – who are even yet supposed to possess remarkable powers of one kind or another. Several families, which have become extinct, are more especially reputed by tradition to have had dealings with the bad spirits, and many of them to have made compacts with the Evil One himself. Amongst the most curious of the stories once told – I believe they are nearly all forgotten – are those connected with Pengerswick [Pengersick] Castle. A small tower alone remains to note the site of a once famous fortified place [see cover photograph].

This castle was said to have been occupied, in the time of Henry VIII, by a man who had committed some great crime; but long previous to that period the place was famous for its wickedness.

How Pengerswick became a sorcerer

The first Pengerswick, by whom the castle, which still bears his name, was built, was a proud man, and desired to ally himself with some of the best families of Cornwall. He wished his son to wed a lady who was very much older than himself, who is said to have been connected with the Godolphin family. This elderly maiden had a violent desire either for the young man or the castle – it is not very clear which. The young Pengerswick gave her no return for the manifestations of love which she lavished upon him. Eventually, finding all her attempts to win the young man's love were abortive, and that all the love potions brewed for her by the Witch of Fraddam were of no avail, she married the old lord – mainly, it is said, to be revenged on the son.

The Witch had a niece who, though poor, possessed considerable beauty; she was called Bitha. This young girl was frequently employed by her aunt and the lady of Godolphin to aid them in their spells on the young Pengerswick, and, as a natural consequence, she fell desperately in love with him herself. Bitha ingratiated herself with the lady of Pengerswick, now the stepmother of the young man, and was selected as her maid. This gave her many opportunities of seeing and speaking to young Pengerswick, and her passion increased. The old stepdame was still passionately fond of the young man, and never let a chance escape her which she thought likely to lead to the excitement of passion in his heart towards her. In all her attempts she failed. Her love was turned to hate; and having seen her stepson in company with Bitha, this hate was quickened by the more violent jealousy. Every means which her wicked mind could devise were employed to destroy the young man. Bitha had learned from her aunt, the Witch of Fraddam, much of her art, and she devoted herself to counteract the spells of her mistress.

The stepmother, failing to accomplish her ends, resolved to ruin young Pengerswick with his father. She persuaded the old man that his son really entertained a violent passion for her, and that she was compelled to confine herself to her tower in fear. The aged woman prevailed on Lord Pengerswick to hire a gang of outlandish sailors to carry his son away and sell him for a slave, giving him to believe that she should herself in a short time present him with an heir.

The young Pengerswick escaped all their plots, and at his own good time he disappeared from the castle, and for a long period was never heard of.

The mistress and maid plotted and counter-plotted to secure the old Pengerswick's wealth; and when he was on his deathbed, Bitha informed him of the vile practices of his wife, and consoled him with the information that he was dying from the effects of poison given him by her.

The young lord, after long years, returned from some Eastern lands with a princess for his wife, learned in all the magic sciences of those enchanted lands. He found his stepmother shut up in her chamber, with her skin covered with scales like a serpent, from the effects of the poisons which she had so often been distilling for the old lord and his son. She refused to be seen, and eventually cast herself into the sea, to the relief of all parties.

Bitha fared not much better. She lived on the Downs in St Hilary; and from the poisonous fumes she had inhaled, and from her dealings with the devil, her skin became of the colour of that of a toad.

Two more versions: the Lord Pengerswick as an enchanter

The Lord of Pengerswick came from some Eastern clime, bringing with him a foreign lady of great beauty. She was considered by all an 'outlandish' woman; and by many declared to be a 'Saracen.' No one, beyond the selected servants, was ever allowed within the walls of Pengerswick Castle; and they, it was said, were bound by magic spells. No one dared tell of anything transacted within the walls; consequently all was conjecture amongst the neighbouring peasantry, miners, and fishermen.

Certain it was, they said, that Pengerswick would shut himself up for days together in his chamber, burning strange things, which sent their strong odours, not only to every part of the castle, but for miles around the country. Often at night, and especially in stormy weather, Pengerswick was heard for hours together calling up the spirits, by reading from his books in some unknown tongue. On those occasions his voice would roll through the halls louder than the surging waves which beat against the neighbouring rocks, the spirits replying like the roar of thunder. Then would all the servants rush in fright from the building, and remain crowded together, even in the most tempestuous night, in one of the open courts.

Fearful, indeed, would be the strife between the man and the demons; and it sometimes happened that the spirits were too powerful for the enchanter. He was, however, constantly and carefully watched by his wife; and whenever the strife became too serious, her harp was heard making the softest, the sweetest music. At this the spirits fled, and they were heard passing through the air towards the Land's End, moaning like the soughing of a departing storm. The lights would then be extinguished in the enchanter's tower, and all would be peace. The servants would return to their apartments with a feeling of perfect confidence. They feared their master, but their mistress inspired them with love.

Lady Pengerswick was never seen beyond the grounds surrounding the castle. She sat all day in lonely state and pride in her tower, the lattice-window of her apartment being high on the seaward side. Her voice accompanying the music of her harp was rarely heard, but when she warbled the soft love strains of her Eastern land. Often at early dawn the very fishes of the neighbouring bay would raise their heads above the surface of the waters, enchanted by the music and the voice; and it is said that the mermaids from the Lizard, and many of the strange spirits of the waters, would come near to Pengerswick cove, drawn by the same influence. On moonlight nights the air has often seemed to be full of sound, and yet the lady's voice was seldom louder than that of a warbling bird. On these occasions, men have seen thousands of spirits gliding up and down the moonbeams, and floating idly on the silvered waves, listening to, and sometimes softly echoing, the words which Lady Pengerswick sang.

Long did this strange pair inhabit this lonely castle; and although the Lord of Pengerswick frequently rode abroad on a most magnificent horse – which had the reputation of being of Satanic origin, it was at once so docile to its master and so wild to any other person – yet he made no acquaintance with any of the neighbouring gentry. He was feared by all, and yet they respected him for many of the good deeds performed by him. He completely enthralled the Giants of the Mount; and before he disappeared from Cornwall, they died, owing, it was said, to grief and want of food.

Where the Lord of Pengerswick came from, no one knew; he, with his lady, with two attendants, who never spoke in any but an Eastern tongue, which was understood by none around them, made their appearance one winter's day, mounted on beautiful horses, evidently from Arabia or some distant land. They soon – having gold in abundance – got possession of a cottage; and in a marvellously short time the castle, which yet bears his name, was rebuilt by this lord. Many affirm that the lord by the force of his enchantments, and the lady by the spell of her voice, compelled the spirits of the earth and air to work for them; and that three nights were sufficient to rear an enormous pile, of which but one tower now remains.

Their coming was sudden and mysterious; their going was still more so. Years had rolled on, and the people around were familiarised with those strange neighbours, from whom also they derived large profits, since they paid whatsoever price was demanded for any article which they required.

One day a stranger was seen in Market-Jew [Marazion, *Marghas Yow*, meaning Thursday Market] whose face was bronzed by long exposure to an Eastern sun. No one knew him; and he eluded the anxious inquiries of the numerous gossips, who were especially anxious to learn something of this man, who, it was surmised by every one, must have some connexion with Pengerswick or his lady; yet no one could assign any reason for such a supposition. Week after week passed away, and the stranger remained in the town, giving no sign. Wonder was on every old woman's lips, and expressed in every old man's eyes; but they had to wonder on.

One thing, it was said, had been noticed; and this seemed to confirm the suspicions of the people. The stranger wandered out on dark nights – spent them, it was thought, on the sea-shore; and some fishermen said they had seen him seated on the rock at the entrance of the valley of Pengerswick. It was thought that the lord kept more at home than usual, and of late no one had heard his incantation songs and sounds; neither had they heard the harp of the lady.

A very tempestuous night, singular for its gloom – when even the ordinary light, which, on the darkest night, is evident to the traveller in the open country, did not exist – appears to have brought things to their climax. There was a sudden alarm in Market-Jew, a red glare in the eastern sky, and presently a burst of flames above the hill, and St Michael's Mount was illuminated in a remarkable manner. Pengerswick Castle was on fire; the servants fled in terror; but neither the lord nor his lady could be found. From that day to the present they were lost to all.

The interior of the castle was entirely destroyed; not a vestige of furniture, books, or anything belonging to the 'Enchanter' could be found. He and everything belonging to him had vanished; and, strange to tell, from that night the bronzed stranger was never again seen. The inhabitants of Market-Jew naturally crowded to the fire; when all was over they returned to their homes, speculating on the strange occurrences of the night. Two of the oldest people always declared that, when the flames were at the highest, they saw two men and a lady floating in the midst of the fire, and that they ascended from amidst the falling walls, passed through the air like lightning, and disappeared.

The Witch of Fraddam and the enchanter of Pengerswick

Again and again had the Lord of Pengerswick reversed the spells of the Witch of Fraddam, who was reported to be the most powerful weird woman in the west country. She had been thwarted so many times by this 'white witch' that she resolved to destroy him by some magic more potent than anything yet heard of. It is said that she betook herself to Kynance Cove, and that there she raised the devil by her incantations, and that she pledged her soul to him in return for the aid he promised.

The enchanter's famous mare was to be seduced to drink from a tub of poisoned water placed by the roadside, the effect of which was to render him in the highest degree restive and cause him to fling his rider. The wounded Lord of Pengerswick was, in his agony, to be drenched, by the old witch, with some hell-broth, brewed in the blackest night, under the most evil aspects of the stars; by this he would be in her power for ever, and she might torment him as she pleased.

The devil felt certain of securing the soul of the Witch of Fraddam, but he was less certain of securing that of the enchanter. They say, indeed, that the sorcery which Pengerswick learned in the East was so potent, that the devil feared him. However, as the proverb is, he 'held with the hounds and ran with the hare'.

The witch collected with the utmost care all the deadly things she could obtain, with which to brew her famous drink. In the darkest night, in the midst of the wildest storms, amidst the flashings of lightnings and the bellowings of the thunder, the witch was seen riding on her black ram-cat over the moors and mountains in search of her poisons. At length all was complete – the horse drink was boiled, the hell-broth was brewed. It was in March, about the time of the equinox; the night was dark, and the King of Storms was abroad. The witch planted her tub of drink in a dark lane, through which she knew the Lord of Pengerswick must pass, and near to it she sat, croning over her crock of broth.

The witch-woman had not long to wait; amidst the hurrying winds was heard the heavy tramp of the enchanter's mare, and soon she perceived the outline of man and horse defined sharply against the line of lurid light which stretched along the western horizon. On they came; the witch was scarcely able to contain herself – her joy and her fears, struggling one with the other, almost overpowered her. On came the horse and his rider: they neared the tub of drink; the mare snorted loudly, and her eyes flashed fire as she looked at the black tub by the roadside.

Pengerswick bent over the horse's neck and whispered into her ear; she turned round, and, flinging out her heels, with one kick she scattered all to the wild winds. The tub flew before the blow; it rushed against the crock, which it overturned, and striking against the legs of the old Witch of Fraddam, she fell along with the tub, which assumed the shape of a coffin. Her terror was extreme: she who thought to have unhorsed the conjuror, found herself in a carriage for which she did not bargain. The enchanter raised his voice and gave utterance to some wild words in an unknown tongue, at which even his terrible mare trembled. A whirlwind arose, and the devil was in the midst of it. He took the coffin in which lay the terrified witch high into the air, and the crock followed them. The derisive laughter of Pengerswick, and the savage neighing of the horse, were heard above the roar of the winds. At length, with a satisfied tone, he exclaimed, 'She is settled till the day of doom,' gave the mare the spurs, and rode rapidly home.

The Witch of Fraddam still floats up and down, over the seas, around the coast, in her coffin, followed by the crock, which seems like a punt in attendance on a jolly-boat. She still works mischief, stirring up the sea with her ladle and broom till the waves swell into mountains, which heave off from their crests so much mist and foam, that these wild wanderers of the winds can scarcely be seen through the mist. Woe to the mariner who sees the witch!

The Lord of Pengerswick alone had power over her. He had but to stand on his tower, and blow three blasts on his trumpet, to summon her to the shore, and compel her to peace.

Trewa, or Trewe: the home of witches

As we walk from Nancledrea Bottoms towards Zennor we pass Trewa, (pronounced 'Truee') which is said to have been the place where at midsummer all the witches of the west met. Here are the remains of very ancient tin stream works, and these, I was informed, 'were the remains of bals which had been worked before the deluge; there was nothing so old anywhere else in Cornwall.' Around us, on the hillsides and up the bottoms, huge boulders of granite are most fantastically scattered. All these rocks sprang from the ground at the call of the giants. At Embla Green we still see the ruins of the Giant's House, but all we know of this Titan is that he was the king. On one side we have the 'Giant's Well', and not far off the 'Druid's Well', and a little before us is Zennor Quoit or cromlech.

From this point the scenery is of the wildest description. The granite cairns are spread around in every direction, and many of those masses are so strangely fashioned by the atmospheric influences ever acting on them, that fancy can readily fashion them into tombs and temples. Rock basins abound on these hills, and of ruined cromlechs there are many.

Whatever the local historians may say, local traditions assure us that on Midsummer Eve all the witches in Penwith gathered here, and that they lit fires on every cromlech, and in every rock basin, until the hills were alive with flame, and renewed their vows to the evil ones from whom they derived their power. Hence, to this day this place is called Burn Downs. Amidst these rock masses there was one pile remarkable amidst all the others for its size, and – being formed of cubical masses – for its square character. This was known as the Witches' Rock, and here it was said they assembled at midnight to carry on their wicked deeds. This rock has been removed, and with it the witches have died, the last real witch in Zennor having passed away, as I have been told, about thirty years since, and with her, some say, the fairies fled. I have, however, many reasons for believing that our little friends have still a few haunts in this locality. There is but one reason why we should regret the disappearance of the Witches' Rock. Any one touching this rock nine times at midnight was insured against bad luck.

Kenidzhek witch

On the tract called the Gump, near Kenidzhek, is a beautiful well of clear water, not far from which was a miner's cot, in which dwelt two miners with their sister. They told her never to go to the well after daylight; they would fetch the water for her. However, on one Saturday night she had forgotten to get in a supply for the morrow, so she went off to the well. Passing by a gap in a broken-down hedge (called a 'gurgo') near the well, she saw an old woman sitting down, wrapped in a red shawl. She asked her what she did there at that time of night, but received no reply; she thought this rather strange, but plunged her pitcher in the well. When she drew it up, though a perfectly sound vessel, it contained no water; she tried again and again, and, though she saw the water rushing in at the mouth of the pitcher, it was sure to be empty when lifted out. She then became rather frightened; spoke again to the old woman, but receiving no answer, hastened away, and came in great alarm to her brothers. They told her that it was on account of this old woman they did not wish her to go to the well at night. What she saw was the ghost of old Moll, a witch who had been a great terror to the people in her lifetime, and had laid many fearful spells on them. They said they saw her sitting in the gap by the wall every night when going to bed.

The witches of the Logan Stone

Who that has travelled into Cornwall but has visited the Logan Stone? Numerous logan rocks exist on the granite hills of the county, but that remarkable mass which is poised on the cubical masses forming its Cyclopean support, at Trereen, is beyond all others 'The Logan Stone'.

A more sublime spot could not have been chosen by the Bardic priesthood for any ordeal connected with their worship; and even admitting that nature may have disposed the huge mass to wear away, so as to rest delicately poised on a pivot, it is highly probable that the wild worship of the untrained tribes, who had passed to those islands from the shores of the Mediterranean Sea, may have led them to believe that some superhuman power belonged to such a strangely balanced mass of rock.

Nothing can be more certain than that through all time, passing on from father to son, there has been a wild reverence of this mass of rock; and long after the days when the Druid ceased to be, there is every reason for believing that the Christian priests, even if they did not encourage, did not forbid the use of this and similar rocks to be used as places of ordeal by the uneducated and superstitious people around.

Hence the mass of rock on which is poised the Logan Stone has ever been connected with the supernatural. To the south of the Logan Rock is a high peak of granite, towering above the other rocks; this is known as the Castle Peak.

No one can say for how long a period, but most certainly for ages, this peak has been the midnight rendezvous for witches. Many a man, and woman too, now sleeping quietly in the churchyard of St Levan, would, had they the power, attest to having seen the witches flying into the Castle Peak on moonlight nights, mounted on the stems of the ragwort, and bringing with them the things necessary to make their charms potent and strong.

This place was long noted as the gathering-place of the army of witches who took their departure for Wales, where they would luxuriate at the most favoured seasons of the year upon the milk of the Welshmen's cows. From this peak many a struggling ship has been watched by a malignant crone, while she has been brewing the tempest to destroy it; and many a rejoicing chorus has been echoed, in horror, by the cliffs around, when the witches have been croaking their miserable delight over the perishing crews, as they have watched man, woman, and child drowning, whom they were presently to rob of the treasures they were bringing home from other lands.

Upon the rocks behind the Logan Rock it would appear that every kind of mischief which can befall man or beast was once brewed by the St Levan witches.

Madgy Figgy's Chair

All those who have visited the fine piles of rocks in the vicinity of St Leven, near the Land's-End, called Tol-Pedn-Penwith [Gwennap Head] and infinitely finer than anything immediately surrounding the most western promontory itself, cannot have failed to notice the arrangement of cubical masses of granite piled one upon the other, known as the 'Chair Ladder'.

This remarkable pile presents to the beat of the Atlantic waves a sheer face of cliff of very considerable height, standing up like a huge basaltic column, or a pillar built by the Titans, the horizontal joints representing so many steps in the so-called 'Ladder'. On the top is placed a stone of somewhat remarkable shape, which is by no great effort of the imagination converted into a chair. There it was that Madgy Figgy, one of the most celebrated of the St Levan and Buryan witches, was in the habit of seating herself when she desired to call up to her aid the spirits of the storm. Often has she been seen swinging herself to and fro on this dizzy height when a storm has been coming home upon the shores, and richly-laden vessels have been struggling with the winds. From this spot she poured forth her imprecations on man and beast, and none whom she had offended could escape those withering spells; and from this 'chair', which will ever bear her name, Madgy Figgy would always take her flight. Often, starting like some huge bird, mounted on a stem of ragwort, Figgy has headed a band of inferior witches, and gone off rejoicing in their iniquities to Wales or Spain.

This old hag lived in a cottage not far from Raftra, and she and all her gang, which appears to have been a pretty numerous crew, were notorious wreckers. On one occasion, Madgy from her seat of storms lured a Portuguese Indiaman into Perloe [Porth Loe?] Cove, and drowned all the passengers. As they were washed on shore, the bodies were stripped of everything valuable, and buried by Figgy and her husband in the green hollow, which may yet be seen, just above Perloe Cove, marking the graves with a rough stone placed at the head of the corpse.

The spoils on this occasion must have been large, for all the women were supplied for years with rich dresses, and costly jewels were seen decking the red arms of the girls who laboured in the fields. For a long time gems and gold continued to be found on the sands. Howbeit, amongst the bodies thrown ashore was one of a lady richly dressed, with chains of gold about her. 'Rich and rare were the gems she wore', and not only so, but valuable treasure was fastened around her, she evidently hoping, if saved, to secure some of her property.

This body, like all the others, was stripped; but Figgy said there was a mark on it which boded them evil, and she would not allow any of the gold or gems to be divided, as it would be sure to bring bad luck if it were separated. A dreadful quarrel ensued, and bloodshed was threatened; but the diabolical old Figgy was more than a match for any of the men, and the power of her impetuous will was superior to them all.

Everything of value, therefore, belonging to this lady was gathered into a heap, and placed in a chest in Madgy Figgy's hut. They buried the Portuguese lady the same evening; and after dark a light was seen to rise from the grave, pass along the cliffs, and seat itself in Madgy's chair at Tol-Pedn. Then, after some hours, it descended, passed back again, and, entering the cottage, rested upon the chest. This curious phenomenon continued for more than three months – nightly – much to the alarm of all but Figgy, who said she knew all about it, and it would all be right in time.

One day a strange-looking and strangely-attired man arrived at the cottage. Figgy's man (her husband) was at home alone. To him the stranger addressed himself by signs – he could not speak English, so he does not appear to have spoken at all – and expressed a wish to be led to the graves. Away they went, but the foreigner did not appear to require a guide. He at once selected the grave of the lady, and sitting down upon it, he gave vent to his pent-up sorrows. He sent Figgy's man away, and remained there till night, when the light arose from the grave more brilliant than ever, and proceeded directly to the hut, resting as usual on the chest, which was now covered up with old sails, and all kinds of fishermen's lumber.

The foreigner swept these things aside, and opened the chest. He selected everything belonging to the lady, refusing to take any of the other valuables. He rewarded the wreckers with costly gifts, and left them – no one knowing from whence he came nor whither he went. Madgy Figgy was now truly triumphant. 'One witch knows another witch, dead or living,' she would say; 'and the African would have been the death of us if we hadn't kept the treasure, whereas now we have good gifts, and no gainsaying 'em.'

Some do say they have seen the light in Madgy Figgy's chair since those times.

Old Madge Figgey and the pig

Madge Figgey once lived in St Leven, but she removed to Buryan Church-town. She had a neighbour, Tom Trenoweth, who had a very fine sow, and the old creature took it into her head to desire this sow. The pig was worth a pound of any man's money, but Madge offered Tom five shillings for it.

'No,' says Tom, 'I shan't sell the sow to you, nor to anybody else. I am going to put her in the house, and feed her for myself against winter.'

'Well,' said old Madge, nodding her head, and shaking her finger at Tom, 'you will wish you had.'

From that time the sow ceased to 'goody' (thrive). The more corn the sow ate, the leaner she became. Old Madge came again, 'Will ye sell her now, Tom?'

'No! and be —— to you,' said Tom.

'Arreah, Tom! you will wish you had, before another week is ended, I can tell ye.' By next week the sow was gone to skin and bone, yet eating all the time meat enough for three.

At last Tom took the sow out of the house, and prepared to drive her to Penzance market, and sell her for what she would fetch.

The rope was put round her leg, but more for fashion's sake than anything else. The poor pig could scarcely stand on her legs, consequently there was little chance of her running away. Well, Tom and his pig were no sooner on the highroad than the sow set off like a greyhound, and never stopped, racing over hedges and ditches, until she reached Leah Lanes. Tom kept hold of the rope till his arm was almost dragged from his body, and he was fairly out of breath. He dropped the rope, piggy went on 'as quiet as a lamb', but only the way which pleased her best. At last Tom and the sow arrived at Tregonebris Downs. At the corner of the roads, where they divide, one going to Sancreed, and the other to Penzance, Tom again laid hold of the rope, and said to himself, 'I'll surely get thee to Penzance yet.'

The moment they came to the market-road, the sow made a bolt, jerked the rope out of Tom's hand, and ran off at full speed, never stopping until she got in under Tregonebris Bridge. Now that bridge is more like a long drain than anything else, and is smallest in the middle; so when the sow got half way in, she stuck fast; she couldn't go forward – she wouldn't come back. Tom fired all the stones he could find, first at the pig's head and then at her tail, and all he got for his pains was a grunt. There he stopped, watching the sow till near sunset; he had eaten nothing since five in the morning, and was starving. He saw no chance of getting the sow out, so he swore at her, and prepared to go home, when who should come by but old Madge Figgey, with her stick in one hand and basket in the other.

'Why, Tom, is that you? What in the world are ye doing here at this time o' day?'

'Well,' says Tom, 'I'm cussed if I can tell; look under the bridge, if you've a mind to know.'

'Why, I hear the sow grunting, I declare. What will ye sell her for now?'

'If you can get her out, take her,' says Tom; 'but hast anything to eat in your basket?'

Madge gave him a twopenny loaf.

'Thank ye,' says Tom. 'Now the devil take the both of ye!'

'Cheat! cheat! cheat!' says Madge. Out came the sow, and followed her home like a dog.

Madam Noy and Old Joan

They say that, a long time since, there lived an old witch down by Alsia Mill, called Joan. Everybody feared to offend the old woman, and gave her everything she looked for, except Madam Noy, who lived in Pendrea.

Madam Noy had some beautiful hens of a new sort, with 'cops' on their heads.

One morning early, Joan comes up to Pendrea, so as to catch Madam Noy going out into the farmyard, with her basket of corn to feed the poultry, and to collect the eggs.

Joan comes up nodding and curtsying every step. 'Good morrow to your honour; how well you are looking, Madam Noy; and, oh, what beautiful hens. I've got an old hen that I do want to set; will you sell me a dozen of eggs? Those with the 'cops' I'd like to have best.'

Madam turned round half offended, and said, 'I have none to sell, neither with the cops nor yet without the cops, whilst I have so many old clucking hens about, and hardly an egg to be found.'

'You surely wouldn't send me home empty as I came, madam dear?'

'You may go home the same way you came, for you aren't wanted here.'

'Now,' croaked Joan, hoarse with passion, 'as true as I tell you so, if you don't sell me some eggs, you will wish your cakes dough.'

As the old witch said this, she perched herself on the stile, shaking her finger and 'nodling' her head.

Madam Noy was a bit of a virago herself, so she took up a stone and flung it at Joan; it hit her in the face, and made her jaws rattle.

As soon as she recovered, she spinned forth:

> 'Madam Noy, you ugly old bitch,
> You shall have the gout, the palsy, and itch;
> All the eggs your hens lay henceforth shall be addle;
> All your hens have the pip, and die with the straddle;
> And ere I with the mighty fine madam have done,
> Of her favourite 'coppies' she shan't possess one.'

From that day forward, madam was always afflicted. The doctor from Penzance could do little for her. The fowls' eggs were always bad; the hens died, and madam lost all her 'coppies'. This is the way it came about – in the place of cops the brains came out – and all by the spells of old Joan.

The Witch of Treva

Once on a time, long ago, there lived at Treva, a hamlet in Zennor, a wonderful old lady deeply skilled in necromancy. Her charms, spells, and dark incantations made her the terror of the neighbourhood. However, this old lady failed to impress her husband with any belief in her supernatural powers, nor did he fail to proclaim his unbelief aloud.

One day this sceptic came home to dinner and found, being exceedingly hungry, to his bitter disappointment, that not only was there no dinner to eat, but that there was no meat in the house. His rage was great, but all he could get from his wife was, 'I couldn't get meat out of the stones, could I?' It was in vain to give the reins to passion, the old woman told him, and he must know 'that hard words buttered no parsnips'.

Well, at length he resolved to put his wife's powers to the proof, and he quietly but determinedly told her that he would be the death of her if she did not get him some dinner; but if in half an hour she gave him some good cooked meat, he would believe all she had boasted of her power, and be submissive to her for ever. St Ives, the nearest market-town, was five miles off; but nothing doubting, the witch put on her bonnet and cloak, and started. Her husband watched her from their cottage door, down the hill, and at the bottom of the hill he saw his wife quietly place herself on the ground and disappear. In her place a fine hare ran on at its full speed.

He was not a little startled, but he waited, and within the half hour in walked his wife with 'good flesh and taties all ready for aiting'. There was no longer any doubt, and the poor husband lived in fear of the witch of Treva to the day of her death.

This event took place after a few years, and it is said the room was full of evil spirits, and that the old woman's shrieks were awful to hear. Howbeit, peace in the shape of pale-faced death came to her at last, and then a black cloud rested over the house when all the heavens were clear and blue.

She was borne to the grave by six aged men, carried, as is the custom, under hand. When they were about half way between the house and the church, a hare started from the roadside and leaped over the coffin. The terrified bearers let the corpse fall to the ground, and ran away. Another lot of men took up the coffin and proceeded. They had not gone far when puss [a hunting term for a hare] was suddenly seen seated on the coffin, and again the coffin was abandoned. After long consultation, and being persuaded by the parson to carry the old woman very quickly into the churchyard, while he walked before, six others made the attempt, and as the parson never ceased to repeat the Lord's Prayer, all went on quietly. Arrived at the church stile, they rested the corpse, the parson paused to commence the ordinary burial service, and there stood the hare, which, as soon as the clergyman began 'I am the resurrection and the life,' uttered a diabolical howl, changed into a black, unshapen creature, and disappeared.

How Mr Lenine gave up courting

Mr Lenine had been, as was his wont, spending his evening hours with the lady of his love. He was a timid man, and always returned to Tregonebris early. Beyond this, as the lady was alone, she deemed it prudent to let the world know that Mr Lenine left her by daylight.

One evening, it was scarcely yet dark and our lover was returning home through Leah Lanes. His horse started at an old woman, who had crept under the hedge for shelter from a passing shower. As Mr Lenine saw a figure moving in the shade he was terrified.

'Tu-whit, tu-whoo, ho,' sang an owl.

'It's only me – Mr Lenine of Tregonebris,' said he, putting the spurs to his horse.

Something followed him, fast as he might go, and he forced his horse up the hill by Leah Vean.

'Tu-whit, tu-whoo, ho,' sang the owl.

'It's only me – Aunt Betty Foss,' screamed the old woman.

'Tu-whit, tu-whoo, ho, ho,' sang the owl again.

'Don't ye be afeard, Mr Lenine,' shrieked Aunt Betty, almost out of breath.

'Tu-whit, tu-whoo, ho, ho, ho,' also shrieked the owl.

'Oh, it's only John Lenine of Tregonebris,' stammered the frightened lover, who had, however, reached home.

He went no more a-courting. He was fully persuaded that either a highwayman and his crew, or the devil and his imps, were upon him. He died a bachelor, and the charming lady became a peevish old maid, and died in solitude; all owing to the hooting owl.

Some do say Betty Foss was a witch, and the owl her familiar.

The witch and the toad

An old woman called Alsey – usually Aunt Alsey – occupied a small cottage in Anthony, one of a row which belonged to a tradesman living in Dock – as Devonport was then designated, to distinguish it from Plymouth. The old woman possessed a very violent temper, and this, more than anything else, fixed upon her the character of being a witch. Her landlord had frequently sought his rent, and as frequently he received nothing but abuse.

He had, on the special occasion to which our narrative refers, crossed the Tamar and walked to Anthony, with the firm resolve of securing his rent, now long in arrears, and of turning the old termagant out of the cottage. A violent scene ensued, and the vicious old woman, more than a match for a really kind-hearted and quiet man, remained the mistress of the situation. She seated herself in the door of her cottage and cursed her landlord's wife, 'the child she was carrying', and all belonging to him, with so devilish a spite that Mr —— owned he was fairly driven away in terror.

On returning home, he, of course, told his wife all the circumstances; and while they were discoursing on the subject – the whole story being attentively listened to by their daughter, then a young girl, who is my informant – a woman came into the shop requiring some articles which they sold.

'Sit still, father,' said Mrs —— to her husband; 'you must be tired. I will see to the shop.'

So she went from the parlour into the shop, and, hearing the wants of her customer, proceeded to supply them, gossiping gaily, as was her wont, to interest the buyer.

Mrs —— was weighing one of the articles required, when something falling heavily from the ceiling of the shop, struck the beam out of her hand, and both – the falling body and the scales – came together with much noise on to the counter. At the same instant both women screamed, the shopkeeper calling also 'Father! father!' – meaning her husband thereby – with great energy.

Mr —— and his daughter were in the shop instantly, and there, on the counter, they saw an enormous and most ugly toad sprawling amidst the chains of the scales. The first action of the man was to run back to the parlour, seize the tongs, and return to the shop. He grasped the swollen toad with the tongs, the vicious creature spitting all the time, and, without a word, he went back and flung it behind the block of wood which was burning in the grate. The object of terror being removed, the wife, who was shortly to become the mother of another child, though usually a woman who had great command over her feelings, fainted.

This circumstance demanding all their attention, the toad was forgotten. The shock was a severe one; and although Mrs —— was restored in a little time to her senses, she again and again became faint. Those fits continuing, her medical attendant, Dr —— , was sent for, and on his arrival he ordered that his patient should be immediately placed in bed, and the husband was informed that he must be prepared for a premature birth.

The anxiety occasioned by these circumstances, and the desire to afford every relief to his wife, so fully occupied Mr —— , that for an hour or two he entirely forgot the cause of all this mischief; or, perhaps satisfying himself that the toad was burnt to ashes, he had no curiosity to look after it. He was, however, suddenly summoned from the bedroom, in which he was with his wife, by his daughter calling to him, in a voice of terror, 'O father, the toad, the toad!'

Mr —— rushed down-stairs, and he then discovered that the toad, though severely burnt, had escaped destruction. It must have crawled up over the log of wood, and from it have fallen down amongst the ashes. There it was now making useless struggles to escape, by climbing over the fender.

The tongs were again put in requisition, with the intention this time of carrying the reptile out of the house. Before, however, he had time to do so, a man from Anthony came hastily into the shop with the information that Aunt Alsey had fallen into the fire, as the people supposed, in a fit, and that she was nearly burnt to death. This man had been sent off with two commissions – one to fetch the doctor, and the other to bring Mr —— with him, as much of the cottage had been injured by fire, communicated to it by the old woman's dress.

In as short a time as possible the parish surgeon and Mr —— were at Anthony, and too truly they found the old woman most severely burnt – so seriously, indeed, there was no chance that one so aged could rally from the shock which her system must have received. However, a litter was carefully prepared, the old woman was placed in it, and carried to the workhouse [workhouses had hospital facilities].

Every attention was given to her situation, but she never recovered perfect consciousness, and during the night she died.

The toad, which we left inside the fender in front of a blazing fire, was removed from a position so trying to any cold-blooded animal, by the servant, and thrown, with a 'hugh' and a shudder, upon one of the flower-beds in the small garden behind the house.

There it lay the next morning dead, and when examined by Mr —— it was found that all the injuries sustained by the toad corresponded with those received by the poor old wretch, who had no doubt fallen a victim to passion.

As we have only to deal with the mysterious relation which existed between the witch and the toad, it is not necessary that we should attend further to the innocent victim of an old woman's vengeance, than to say that eventually a babe was born – that that babe grew to be a handsome man, was an officer in the navy, and having married, went to sea, and perished, leaving a widow with an unborn child to lament his loss. Whether this was a result of the witch's curse, those who are more deeply skilled in witchcraft than I am may perhaps tell.

The sailor wizard

This appears to have been, and it may still be, a very common superstition. I have lately received from Mr Thomas Quiller Couch of Bodmin the story of some sailors, who had reason to suspect that one of their body was a wizard. This was eventually proved to have been the case, by circumstances in every way resembling those of our old witch. There had been a quarrel, and revenge had been talked of. The sailors were all grouped together in the forepart of the ship, except the suspected one, and a toad fell sprawling amongst them. One of the men flung the creature into the fire in the caboose [on-deck kitchen]. It struggled for a moment in the fire, and then by a convulsive effort flung itself out. Immediately the toad was caught up by one of the men, and flung into the sea.

In the course of some little time the absent sailor made his appearance dripping wet. In a drunken frolic he had first fallen into the fire at a low beer shop or kiddlywink, and subsequently he fell out of the boat into the sea.

The Zennor charmers

Both men and women in this parish possessed this power to a remarkable degree. They could stop blood, however freely it might be flowing. 'Even should a pig be sticked in the very place, if a charmer was present, and "thought" of his charm at the time, the pig would not bleed.' This statement, made by a Zennor man, shows a tolerably large amount of faith in their power.

The charmers are very cautious about communicating their charms. A man would not on any account tell his charm to a woman, or a woman communicate hers to a man. People will travel many miles to have themselves or their children charmed for 'wildfires' (erysipelas) ringworms, pains in the limbs or teeth, or 'kennels' on the eyes (ulcerations).

A correspondent writes me: 'Near this lives a lady charmer, on whom I called. I found her to be a really clever, sensible woman. She was reading a learned treatise on ancient history. She told me there were but three charmers left in the west, one at New Mill, one in Morvah, and herself.'

J — H — , the Conjurer of St Columb

This old man was successful in persuading his dupes that he owed his powers over evil spirits to his superior learning and his unblemished life. This assumption of piety was well preserved, and to the outside world his sanctity was undoubted. The only practice which can be named as peculiar to H —— was that of lighting scores of candles and placing them around the meadow near his house. Of course such a display would attract much attention; and J —— succeeded in conveying an impression to the minds of the country people that this process was required to counteract the spells of the witches.

When this old fellow has been summoned, as he often was, to the houses supposed to be under the influence of evil, or to be bewitched, his practice was not a little original, though wanting in all that dignifies the office of an exorcist. When he arrived at the house, before speaking to any one, he would commence operations by beating with a heavy stick on the wooden partitions, screens, or pieces of furniture, so as to make the greatest possible noise, shouting loudly all the time, 'Out! out! out! Away! away! away! to the Red Sea – to the Red Sea – to the Red Sea.' Frequently he would add, with violent enunciation and much action, a torrent of incoherent and often incomprehensible words (locally, 'gibberish'). The proceeding being brought to a close, and the spirits of evil flown, every part of the house was ordered to be well cleansed, and the walls and ceilings to be thoroughly lime-washed – certainly the only sensible part of the whole operation.

When J —— H —— was applied to respecting stolen property, his usual practice was to show the face of the thief in a tub of water. J —— drove a considerable trade in selling powders to throw over bewitched cattle.

(*When cattle or human beings have been bewitched, it was very commonly thought that if a bottle of urine from the diseased beast or person was obtained, then corked very tight and buried mouth downwards, that the witch would be afflicted with strangury, and in her suffering confess her crime and beg forgiveness.*)

In relation to this subject, and confirming an opinion already expressed in the existence still of a belief in magic and charms, I print the following communication from a lady of considerable literary ability:

Several years ago, while residing at Falmouth, I remember to have heard of a man in humble life, named Thomas Martin, whose abode was said to be at a village in the neighbourhood of Redruth, and who accomplished wonderful cures of children subject to fits, or personally injured by any deformity, by his power of charming.

This man also practised soothsaying to a considerable extent, and revealed, with unquestionable accuracy, where articles mysteriously abstracted were concealed. If a cow suddenly lost her milk, whether witchcraft had exerted its malignant influence on the non-producing animal or no, such a personage could not but exercise an important power over the rustic population of the neighbourhood. But belief in the mysterious intelligence of Martin was by no means confined to the peasant class.

A highly-respected and even ladylike person told the writer, with all the gravity becoming such a communication, that she had once made an appointment with Thomas Martin to meet him at a certain stile, for the purpose of receiving from him the prediction of her future lot – in other words, having her fortune told; and hastening thither at the time appointed, was horrified to find the stile occupied by a large black snake. As Martin did not make his appearance, she inferred that he had assumed the serpent form, and not being disposed to hold any intercourse with a being of such questionable exterior, she hastened away, determined never more to risk the attainment of the knowledge she coveted through a probably diabolic channel.

This anecdote is given as veritable experience of the belief which may prevail in a mind fairly intelligent, and generally rational in conducting the ordinary business of life.

Martin's reputation was disputed by no one, and that it continued unimpaired to the close of his life reflects no inconsiderable credit on the shrewdness and sagacity of his mind and his power of guessing.

In the town where the writer has been residing for the last four months, there is a female, advanced in years and of good character, who, according to the report of many persons – one a relative of her own – is peculiarly endowed with the power of charming away the disease called the 'kennel,' an infection of the eye, which causes extreme pain. A young lady's father was one evening suffering severe pain in the right eye, and after trying various remedies without effect, the agony having greatly increased, in her despair she sought an occasion to leave the house, and hastened at once to the abode of the charmer.

She told her errand to the woman, who said that many had come to her for the purpose of ridiculing her, and she did not like to say anything about charming — she did not wish to be laughed at. On this the young lady assured her that her object in true faith was to obtain relief for her suffering father, and by no means to indulge the spirit of ridicule.

On this representation she was satisfied, and desired to know the 'kind' of kennel which affected the gentleman's eye. This information the daughter was unable to give her, being unacquainted with their peculiarities. 'Because,' said the charmer, 'there are nine kinds of kennels', intimating at the same time that a different charm might be said or applied to each, so that to avoid omitting any she must say the charms for all, in order that the one especially affecting the diseased eye should be certainly included in the charm.

She went upstairs, and remained about half an hour. On her return she addressed the young lady, and told her she might go home, where she would learn whether the eye had been relieved. She took no money for her incantation. Any little present might be offered at a subsequent visit, but no direct payment was ever requested, and indeed would have been declined.

The amazement and pleasure of the anxious daughter, on her arrival at home, will be imagined, on learning from her father that the intense pain in the eye had ceased during her absence, though he had not been made acquainted with her errand. The influence of the faith of another, in this case, on the relief of the afflicted person, has no verisimilitude save with that of the father of the demoniac in the gospel, or the removal of the son's fever in consequence of the faith of the father. I have no reason whatever to question the truth of this story, which was confirmed by the wife of the gentleman thus relieved.

The slippery slope

A still more curious instance of the effect of charm, though quite of another character, was related to me by the same party. The gentleman referred to being much afflicted with cramp, his wife was earnestly advised, by a country woman to whom she mentioned the circumstance, to request her husband to place his slippers, with the toes turned upward, at the foot of the bed. Half smiling at the wise counsel, yet perhaps not altogether incredulous, he followed the good woman's advice, and to his great comfort found himself unaffected by his dreaded enemy throughout the night.

His faith being thus established in the 'anti-cramp' influence of upturned slippers, he took care to place them, or to have them placed, in the prescribed attitude on several successive nights. One night, however, he was again seized with some appalling twinges, and bethinking himself of the cause, suddenly recollected that in hastening into bed he had not observed the important rule; instantly he had the slippers restored to their proper position, and, to his astonishment and delight, the pain ceased, and visited him no more.

After this experience of the wonderful effects that followed so simple a specific, it may be easily imagined that he did not again risk the return of the cramp from neglecting it. Such phenomena seem beyond the power of explanation on any known medical principles. If anyone more than usually versed in the subtle power exercised on the body by the mind, can throw light on the 'slipper' cure of the cramp, he will deserve much at the hands of physiological and mental science.